Meet the Mammals

CONTENTS

What Is a

Leopard

Mammal?

Dog and puppies

Bear

There are many kinds of animals in the world. One group of animals is called mammals.

All mammals have hair or fur. All mammals feed their babies with mother's milk. All mammals are warm-blooded.

Most mammals live on land.
Some mammals live in the water.
Dolphins are mammals. Whales
are mammals, too.

Giraffes

There are even flying mammals, like bats. And guess what? People are mammals, too! 🐘

Dolphin

Raccoon

BIG

AND   SMALL

Shrew

Mammals come in all sizes. Whales are the biggest mammals on Earth. They can be 100 feet long! That's longer than two school buses.

Shrews are one of the earth's smallest mammals. They live in the woods. Shrews can be just two inches long! That's about the size of your finger. 🐘

Whale

A Joey Grows Up

A kangaroo is a special kind of mammal. The mother has a pouch where her baby lives. The pouch is like a pocket.

A baby kangaroo is called a joey. The joey rides, sleeps, and drinks milk in the pouch. He does not even peek out until he is five months old.

The joey eats and grows.

When a joey is born, he is the size
of a lima bean. He has no hair. He
doesn't even look like a kangaroo. The
joey stays safe in his mother's pouch.

A joey jumps out of the pouch when he is six months old. He begins to eat grass and hop like his mother.

The joey still sleeps in the pouch.
But soon, he will leave it for good.
He will be ready to live on his own.

Khana
the Tiger

Khana is feeling so bored. Her mother has gone hunting for food. Hunting is very dangerous, so Khana must stay in a safe place.

Khana wants to play. What's that?
Something is moving in the grass.
She trots over to see. It's a beautiful
butterfly.

Khana tries to touch the butterfly, but it darts away. She scampers after it. Again and again she tries to catch it with her paw.

Khana is lost! She has chased the butterfly for such a long way. And now it is raining. She sits down and cries like a kitten.

Suddenly there's a noise! Khana looks up, frightened. A huge elephant is lumbering toward her. It's the biggest animal she has ever seen.

Khana turns and runs faster than she has ever run before. She is running like the wind, and crying for her mother.

Khana hears her mother's roar and runs to meet her. Khana's mother is very angry. But Khana is so pleased to see her again.

Khana's mother soon forgives her. They lie down, and Khana climbs onto her. She purrs happily, feeling safe once more.

You've been reading about different kinds of mammals.

Here are some more mammals: cat, deer, cow, horse, lion.

You can make your own mammal book. Here's how.

You Will Need

❑ paper
❑ crayons
❑ pencil
❑ stapler

I. Draw a picture of a mother mammal and her baby.

pandas

cats

whales

3. Now draw more mammals and their babies for your mammal book.

mal Book

- **Under the picture, print ir name.**

- **Make a cover for your ok and staple the pages gether.**

Share your mammal book with your friends.

Tell a story about the mammals in your book. You or your teacher can write the story.

Wake Up, Bears

A bear makes a den in the fall.

Bear cubs are born in the winter inside the den.

Bears make a den in the fall. They sleep there all winter. They do not eat or drink. The bear cubs are born in the den. They nurse until spring.

Cubs sleep in the den with their mother until spring.

Wake up, bears! It's spring. Now the bears leave their den. The cubs stay near their mother. She shows them what to eat. She chases them up a tree if there is danger. Next fall, the cubs will find their own den. 🐘

Bears look for plants, fruit, and nuts to eat.

Bear cubs can climb fast. They are safe in a tree.

Grandpa Bear's Lullaby

The night is long
But fur is deep.
You will be warm
In winter sleep.

The food is gone
But dreams are sweet
And they will be
Your winter meat.

The cave is dark
But dreams are bright
And they will serve
As winter light.
Sleep, my little cubs, sleep.

Jane Yolen

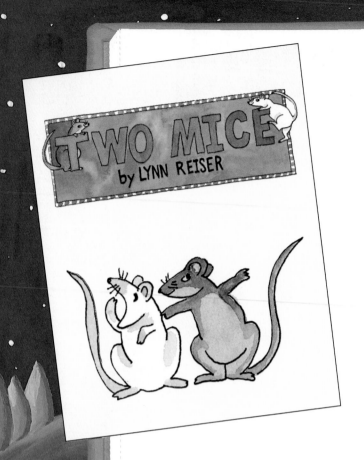

TWO MICE

Once there were
two mice who lived
beside a window.

One lived inside
the window,
in a cage
on top of
a bookshelf.

One lived outside
the window,
in a mouse hole
under a rosebush.

The inside mouse
ate mouse food from a bowl,
drank water from a bottle,
and ran around a wheel.

The outside mouse
ate strawberries
and acorns,
drank raindrops
from rose leaves,
and ran in and out
the mouse hole,
and up and down
and around
the rosebush.

One night the window
was open.
The outside mouse
ran inside.

Inside, the two mice
ate mouse food from the bowl,
drank water from the bottle,
and ran around the wheel—
that was all.

  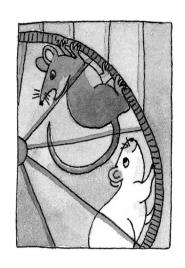

One mouse
was content.

One mouse was
ready for more.

The outside mouse ran
out the window.
The inside mouse followed.

The two mice
ate a strawberry—

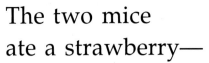

and a snake almost ate them.

They nibbled an acorn—

and a raccoon
almost nibbled
them.

They drank
raindrops from
a rose leaf—

and an owl
almost carried
them off to
its nest.

One mouse was
ready for a nap.

One mouse was
ready for more.

The window was open.
The inside mouse ran inside.
The outside mouse did not follow.

The outside mouse ran
in and out the mouse hole,
and up and down and
around the rosebush,
playing "catch me if you can"
with the snake, the raccoon,
and the owl.

The inside mouse took a nap.

Some like to live in one place— and some like to live in another place.

Some might like to do both.

CHECK IT OUT!

Two Bear Cubs
by Ann Jonas

Two baby bears lose their mother. Where will they find her? Read and find out.

Sebastian Lives in a Hat
by Thelma Catterwell and Kerry Argent

Sebastian is a baby wombat who was rescued from the wild. Read this book to find out how he grows up.

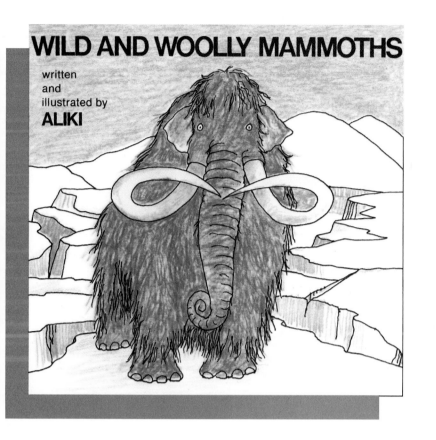

Wild and Wooly Mammoths
by Aliki

Mammoths were huge mammals that lived a long time ago. This book will tell you lots more about them.

Hi, Cat!
by Ezra Jack Keats

Archie meets a cat and the suprises start happening.

KOSMIC, the

Travis lives in Florida with his family and his best friend, Kosmic. Kosmic is a dog. Travis and Kosmic are together almost all the time.

Travis was born with weak arms and legs. He can't walk very well. Kosmic is trained to help Travis get around and do things.

Wonder Dog

Kosmic helps Travis go places. They go to school together. Kosmic opens doors and carries books in a backpack. She helps Travis get up if he falls.

Travis likes school. During the day, Kosmic rests under his desk. She is trained to be very quiet and still. But she is always ready to help Travis.

When Kosmic is on the job, she listens only to Travis. Nobody else can talk to or play with her while she's working. She must always be ready for Travis.

Before Kosmic came to help Travis, there were lots of things he could not do. Now, thanks to Kosmic, Travis can do almost anything. They make a great team! 🐘

Last Look